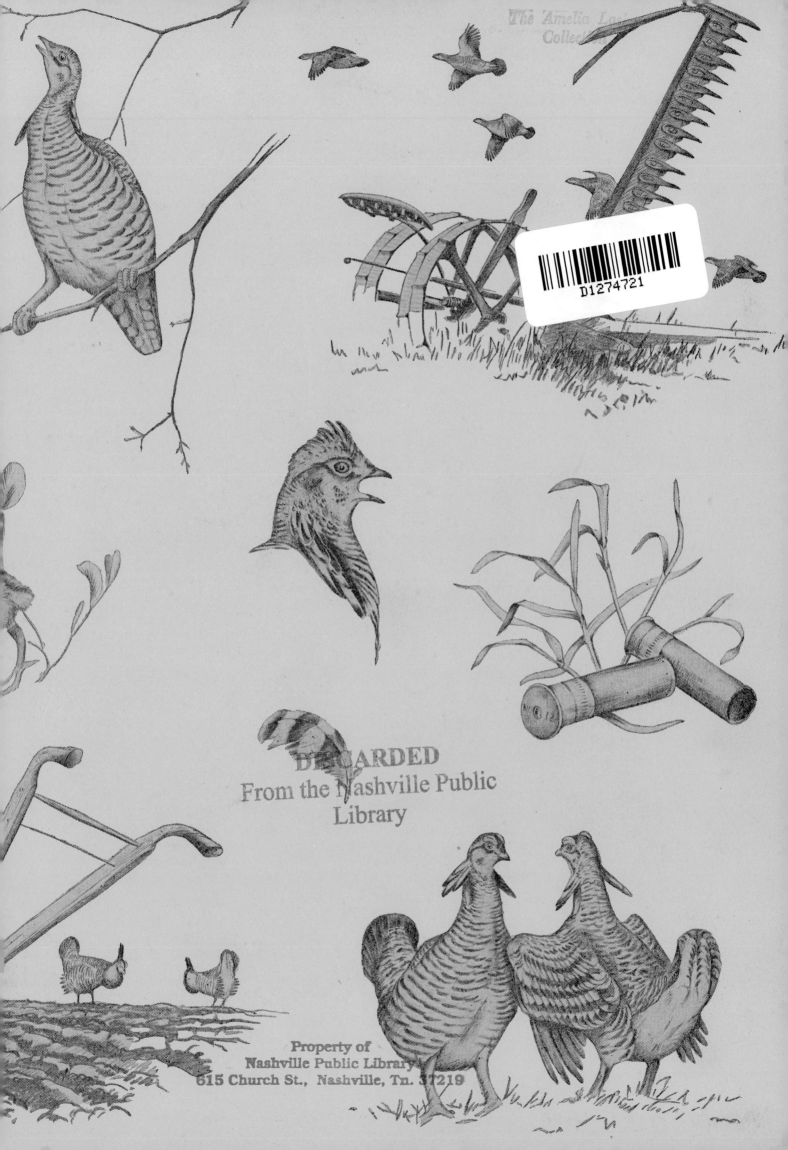

THE
PRAIRIE CHICKEN
IN MISSOURI

By

CHARLES W. SCHWARTZ

Published By
CONSERVATION COMMISSION
STATE OF MISSOURI

TO ARTHUR LINCOLN CLARK

Former Chief, Division of Fish, Game and Forests,

Missouri Conservation Commission

who fostered with foresight and imagination
a pioneer program of wildlife management
on the land—

who, until his untimely death on September
20, 1944, on the eve of its publication, guided
and made possible both the preparation of
"The Prairie Chicken in Missouri" and the
study upon which it is based—

THIS BOOK IS DEDICATED, WITH DEEP RESPECT.

F O R E W O R D

Here are new pages for our old American family album. These portraits of the prairie chicken, lineal descendant of one of our first families, are as reminiscent of the pioneer days as the shadowy old daguerreotype and crayon portraits of our sturdy forefathers. For the prairie chicken, now little more than a tradition to the oncoming generation, was companion to the trackless prairie, the virgin forests, and the covered wagon when the white man first opened up this rich wilderness of natural resources. And like the vanishing forests and wasted soils, the prairie chicken has taken its beating and retreated as commercial exploitation advanced. It now remains as a symbol of our continent as it used to be. Its booming at dawn and dusk is now only a faint echo of the days of the covered wagon. In its sparse survival lies a romantic story.

That the prairie chicken is now to be seen at all is one of the miracles of nature's persistence and a tribute to those who believe that by wise management and understanding we can retain both the beauties of nature and the comforts of civilization.

Those who care to look for it will find hidden behind these exquisite studies of the life history of the prairie chicken the secret of both the cause and the cure for many of our losing battles for conservation. The formula for preservation and restoration rests primarily on our accurate knowledge of the habits and environment of our native wildlife species. Without the application of this knowledge they cannot prosper, and the State of Missouri is to be congratulated for emergence from its indifference to waste to its now recognized position as highest exponent of state management of wildlife resources.

It is a happy circumstance that the drudgery of biological research and labor of restoration can be illumminated by such a handsome and instructive exhibit.

J. N. Darling

ALIAS

Ding

P R E F A C E

This volume is presented as a result of three years of study of the prairie chicken in the state of Missouri by Charles W. Schwartz, the author, artist, and photographer.

The study has been conducted as a part of the Federal Aid to Wildlife Program of the Conservation Commission of Missouri with the cooperation of the United States Fish and Wildlife Service of the Department of the Interior. The major objective of that program has been to develop a long-term, comprehensive plan of wildlife management for each region in the state. Also, by conducting certain special studies, to develop management recommendations for the species presenting the most difficult problems. The program started in December, 1938, and has been carried on, according to plan, for a period of approximately five years terminating June 30, 1943.

The special study of the prairie chicken began in July of 1940 and has been conducted in coordination with the other related studies, which, together, comprise the complete research program directed toward the correlation of wildlife management practices with the economic interests in soil as the basic resource and with its conservation and use.

Intensive work on the prairie chicken project on a full-time basis had been completed in June, 1943, to the point of determining the life history of the bird in Missouri and of furnishing the necessary background for management purposes. The services of Mr. Schwartz, therefore, have now been directed to another project in a broader field of wildlife research, but this will not prevent him from continuing certain additional studies of the prairie chicken.

The Conservation Commission offers this volume in the hope that it will present a clear, simplified but technically accurate story in a manner which can be grasped and interpreted by young folks and adults, and which may stimulate interest and action toward the further restoration of this magnificient bird.

I. T. BODE, Director
CONSERVATION COMMISSION
State of Missouri

ACKNOWLEDGMENTS

Ever since that April morning when I first witnessed the courtship drama of the prairie chickens silhouetted against the sunrise, it has been my wish to present it to others. In partial fulfillment of that desire, this book is an attempt to portray the prairie chicken as I have come to know it. It is hoped that the photographs, selected from many hundreds taken, may furnish both information and enjoyment.

My introduction to the prairie chicken came as a biologist on the staff of the Missouri Conservation Commission in 1940, when I was assigned to a study of the species under the Pittman-Robertson, Federal Aid—Wildlife Program. My wife, Dr. Elizabeth Reeder Schwartz, shared with me the planning, toil, and suspense involved in bringing the subject before my camera, and she has helped at all stages in the preparation of this book. I am indebted to the members of the Missouri Conservation Commission, to Mr. I. T. Bode, Director, and to all of my associates on the staff who have given encouragement and help, particularly to Mr. Arthur L. Clark, Chief, Division of Fish, Game, and Forests, who was instrumental in proposing a program in the field of wildlife research which permitted this study to be made, and to Mr. Paul Q. Tulenko, State Project Leader, who has guided this book through the many tedious steps involved in publication.

Dr. Rudolf Bennitt, Professor of Zoology, University of Missouri, contributed constructive suggestions during the study and helpful assistance in the preparation of the text. Special thanks are due Mr. Edward K. Love of St. Louis, a member of the Commission, who has personally underwritten the cost of publication, giving thereby still further evidence of his generous and loyal support of Missouri's wildlife program.

As a technical note, the photographs were taken with a Leica camera, employing 50 mm., 90 mm. telephoto, and 200 mm. telephoto lenses. The film was Eastman Panatomic X, developed in Edwal 12.

Charles W. Schwartz

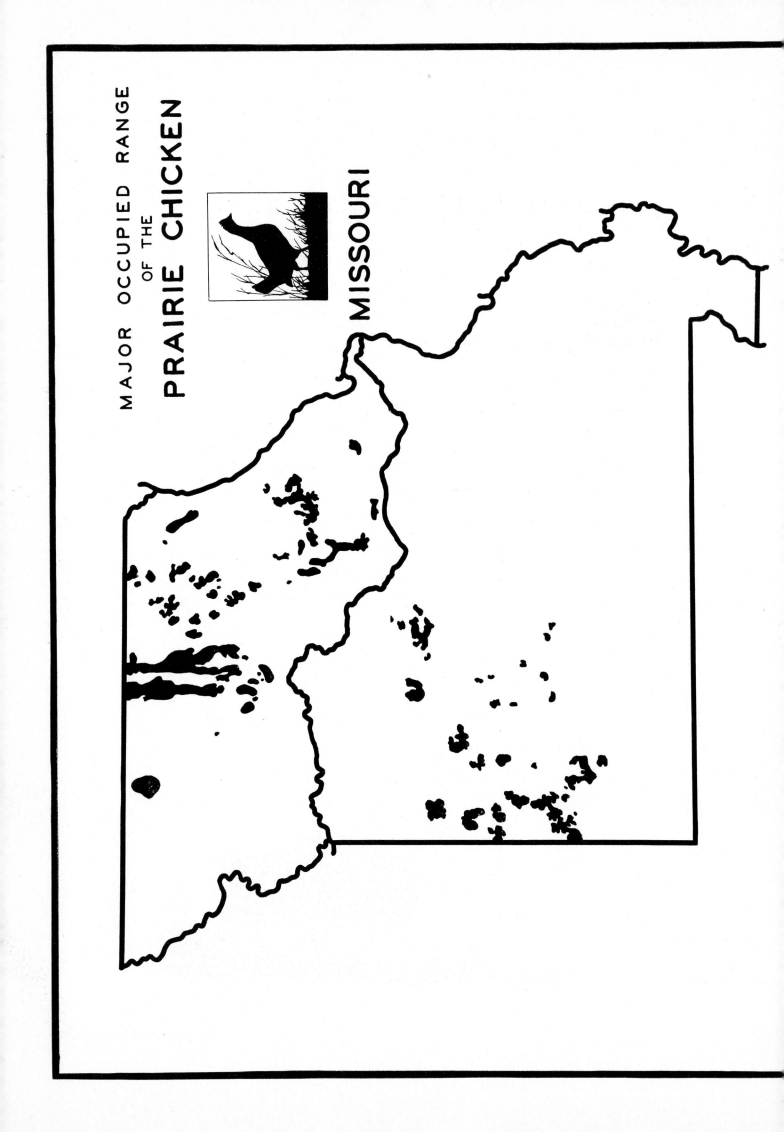

MAJOR OCCUPIED RANGE OF THE PRAIRIE CHICKEN

MISSOURI

INTRODUCTION

 Less than seventy-five years ago, the resonant booming call of the greater prairie chicken could be heard each spring throughout the prairies of Missouri and even on some open ridges of the Ozarks. Today this species occupies only about twenty-five hundred square miles or one tenth of its original range in the state. The population likewise has dwindled from countless numbers to approximately thirteen thousand birds. To understand their present distribution and status it is necessary to consider the soil and the history of its changing use.

In their original condition, the glaciated and wind-laid soils of northern Missouri and the residual soils of the southwest supported a vast prairie composed of dense stands of big and little bluestem grasses with their associated flora and fauna. The only breaks in the landscape were narrow bands of timber and brush bordering the streams and draws in the shallow valleys.

During the last half of the nineteenth century almost all of the virgin prairie sod was torn apart by the plow; the tall and graceful bluestem, which had covered the land since time immemorial, gave way to corn and small grains that left the soil bare for months at a time. Although the prairie chicken exhibits wide tolerance and a high degree of adaptability to changing conditions, it could not endure the destruction of most of its range or the ravages of market hunters who took an inconceivable toll during this period. So great was the loss,—to nature and man together—that in 1907 only about twelve thousand five hundred birds were believed to be left in the state; therefore, the season was closed.

Gradually it was realized that a system of intensive cultivation was too much of a drain on most Missouri prairie soils. Only the level and most fertile soils in the northwestern part of the state were found to be suitable for continuous cropping, a system that definitely excluded prairie chickens. Much of the remaining prairie soil, because of its low fertility, erosive nature, or poor drainage, was returned to the use to which it is best suited—livestock production with the hay and pasture that such a program involves.

As a result of these changes, prairie chickens at present are restricted to the few areas whose native sod has never been plowed and to those parts of the prairie that were once cultivated but have now been returned to permanent grassland.

During the period of changing land use, the population has fluctuated between five thousand and fifteen thousand birds, following a rather uniform cyclic pattern. Their current status is probably influenced also by this cyclic condition, as well as by improved legal protection and by recent agricultural trends which foster increased acreages of permanent grassland.

It is this grassland, when properly managed, that furnishes the cover so vital to their nesting, roosting, and other requirements. Thus the basic structure of the soil, its fertility, and the topography set the pattern of land use which in turn defines the present and future distribution, and to a great extent the numbers, of the prairie chicken in Missouri.

A SPECIES worthy of attention.

As EARLY as January, prairie chicken cocks may be seen silhouetted against the sunrise as they begin their elaborate courtship display. Their meeting places are known as booming grounds because it is here that the males utter their resonant booming call. Booming is feeble and infrequent early in the year, but it increases in vigor and frequency as the season advances. During periods of severe cold and raw weather these morning performances may be discontinued, but as winter merges into spring the cocks gather regularly twice a day. The morning meetings begin about half an hour before sunrise and last for two or three hours. In the evening the birds convene an hour or so before sunset and remain until dusk. These performances continue until June.

Almost all booming grounds are situated on open ridges or slight "rises" on the prairie, and their locations generally remain unchanged from year to year. Some are known to have been occupied regularly for at least forty years, while others have been used more intermittently. The birds tolerate many disturbances, even the establishment of a road directly through the center of their stage, as in this photograph.

Most booming grounds have a cover of permanent grass, but some are continued in use even after the original sod is broken for cultivation. An observation blind is in the center of the booming ground in this field of barley.

THE COVER on booming grounds in pastures and meadows is usually sparser and lower than the surrounding vegetation. The size and shape of a booming ground are influenced by cover conditions, topography, and the number of birds which use it, while the number and distribution of booming grounds vary with the size of the occupied area and the density of the prairie chicken population.

Only cocks occupy the booming grounds regularly throughout the spring. The numbers found on different grounds vary from two to forty-two, averaging twelve. They also rise and fall with yearly changes in the population level. The attendance of cocks is irregular at first; but at mid-season, when courting is at its peak, they seldom miss a day.

ONE OF the most spectacular features of the booming ground display is the performance which accompanies the booming call. As a prelude, the cock usually runs forward a short distance, stops suddenly, and stamps his feet rapidly in a dance, sometimes pivoting in a half or full circle. During the dance, whose steps occasionally can be heard a hundred feet away, his brilliant orange air sacs begin to inflate and he erects his long neck feathers (pinnae). His tail, spread fanwise, snaps suddenly with a sharp "click," and the booming begins. The fleshy orange eyebrows are usually prominent during the booming performance.

THE QUALITY of the booming is like that of the lower notes of an ocarina or the sound made by blowing across the open neck of a bottle. In the fully-developed call there are three notes, rising at even intervals of a quarter- or half-tone. The lowest note is seldom below the first E-flat above middle C; the highest is seldom above the next G. The interval of the entire call is usually not over one full tone, and the three notes together last two or three seconds. They might be written as follows: "oo - loo - woo." The call often has a curious ventriloquial character and may be heard easily a mile away on a calm day. The sound is produced in the voice box (syrinx) and is amplified by resonance in the air sacs. When many birds are booming at once, the calls from a booming ground blend into one continuous, almost a humming, sound.

Booming seems to serve three purposes: It announces the presence of males to females in the vicinity. When females are on the booming ground, it is part of the display which appears to attract a hen into the male's individual preserve. It may also intimidate other males, since cocks frequently boom before one another.

O<small>N THE</small> booming ground, each male estab-
lishes a "territory" whose boundaries are somewhat flexible but are
maintained by successive bouts with nearby cocks. Each cock is master
in his own territory and most of his booming and mating are done
there. Territorial disputes are accompanied by high-pitched cackles,
peculiar grunts, and much wing-slapping as the contestants seesaw
back and forth. These fights occur throughout the spring, but they
are most spirited and frequent early in the season.

Sometimes two cocks charge toward each other, apparently bent on combat. Then for no obvious reason, they may stop suddenly, stare at each other and walk quietly away, or settle down a few feet apart and "talk" it over.

Occasionally the disputes are more violent, the birds jumping several feet into the air and striking with their wings, feet, and bills. Little harm is done and the most serious result is seldom more than a few missing feathers or a gash in an air sac.

During the spring, in contrast to the nervous and belligerent attitude of the male, the female appears calm and deliberate. Her dark-brown and tan markings are almost identical to those of the cock, but she lacks the brilliant orange air sacs and eyebrows, and her pinnae are much shorter. Also her tail feathers are cross-barred, while those of the male are more nearly uniform in color.

FEMALES do not visit the booming ground until late in March, and even then only one or two may appear for a few minutes. Each of these early visits is heralded by the assembled cocks with a series of explosive cackles, as the male performers outdo themselves in dancing and booming, and territorial boundaries are ignored in their rush toward the hen. The female, however (left center in the photograph), appears indifferent and rarely allows mating so early in the season. If attempts are made, they are as a rule violently interrupted by competing males.

THE NUMBER of females visiting a booming ground increases until early April, when a constant and maximum number appear regularly for about a week. As many as eighteen hens have been observed on a booming ground occupied at the time by twenty-eight cocks. It is at this "height of the season" that most of the mating takes place. In contrast to their earlier disregard of territorial boundaries when an occasional female visited the booming ground, the cocks now maintain a regular territorial pattern. The hens disperse themselves over the booming ground during part of the daily period, visiting the cocks in their territories. Eight hens and eleven cocks are shown in this photograph.

AT INTERVALS during the height of the booming season, the females gather into a loose flock near the center of the booming ground. Here, surrounded by the cocks, they move about in leisurely fashion, sometimes stopping to harass or peck at other hens in the flock. They are now very receptive to the attentions of the males and often manifest their readiness to mate by assuming the mating position. The cocks adjacent to this area mate more often than those whose territories are farther removed.

In the presence of a hen the cock booms more frequently than before and displays continuously. The female, although seemingly indifferent to these attentions, nevertheless shows her interest by remaining within his territory.

MATING, which is promiscuous, is sometimes preceded by only the booming display, but more often, at the height of the season, an elaborate bowing ceremony takes place. The cock prostrates himself with wings outstretched and bill touching the ground.

THE NUPTIAL bow may be repeated several times between brief periods of booming. It is rarely given except at the height of the season, and never except in the presence of a hen.

FOLLOWING the booming and bowing performances, the female signifies her acceptance by assuming the mating position. The cock pauses momentarily before mounting.

As the male mounts, the female raises her wings and waves them slowly.

At the height of the booming season matings are seldom interrupted, even when not all of the males have hens within their territories. All of the females are probably successfully mated early in April, fulfilling the purpose of the booming ground. Thereafter the number of female visitors declines rapidly, and the occasional attempted matings are once more regularly interrupted by other males. At the same time, the activity of the males also diminishes until early June, when they cease to use the booming grounds.

AFTER mating, the hen selects the nest site. This is determined to a large extent by the presence of suitable cover on ungrazed meadows and lightly-grazed pastures in the vicinity of the booming ground.

THE IMMEDIATE nesting cover is primarily grassy. However, occasionally nests are located in blackberry or dewberry patches which provide additional concealment and shelter, although many nests have little or no cover overhead.

Most of the nests are on slopes in the rolling prairie or on slightly elevated and well-drained spots in the more level prairie.

Laying begins about the middle of April, but incubation is not begun until early May when the clutch of eggs is completed.

THE NEST is about seven inches in diameter and only two or three inches deep. It is not an elaborate structure and is rather flimsily built of dead grass. The full clutch usually contains from twelve to sixteen eggs, although there may be any number between eight and twenty-five. It is possible that the larger clutches may have been laid by two hens. Although they vary somewhat, the eggs usually measure about one and three-quarters by one and one-quarter inches. In color they are uniformly tan, sometimes flecked with tiny brown and red spots.

DURING the early part of the incubation period the female is wary and easily flushed from the nest, but as hatching time approaches she is reluctant to leave, relying upon her concealing coloration.

THE HEN usually leaves early in the morning and late in the evening for short periods of feeding. She does not cover the nest and thus it is exposed only when the light is dim. Most nests, however, are less exposed than the one shown in this photograph.

THE INCUBATION period is twenty-three days, but from eight to twenty-four hours may elapse between pipping of the first egg and departure of the brood from the nest. Most hatchings occur during the last week of May and first week of June, although some are completed as late as mid-July. Both fertility and hatching success are high.

THE CHICKS are highly precocial. Within a few hours after all the eggs have hatched, the chicks leave the nest accompanied by the hen.

THE NEWLY-HATCHED birds are covered with greenish-yellow down splotched with black. The "egg tooth" is present at hatching but disappears within twenty-four hours. After leaving the nest, the chicks never range more than a few yards from the hen and return frequently for brooding. The first few days are spent near the nest, although the family tends to move gradually toward the nearby swales. The chicks begin at once to feed upon small insects and are adept at pursuing and capturing them.

WHEN the chicks are about two weeks old, the family ranges farther afield and gradually moves toward higher ground and fields of small grain, where they remain until the harvest in late June or early July.

At three or four weeks of age the young birds, now known as poults, can make sustained flights of about fifty yards. In another week their flying radius increases to about one hundred yards. The size of the family is now smaller, indicating some loss of young birds. After the grain harvest the broods frequent shady areas along the field borders. The chicks begin to molt when about six weeks of age, and the brood begins to break up about a month later.

W<small>HILE</small> the females are occupied with their broods, the cocks move about as individuals or small groups. The daily range of a single male, as in the spring, is probably not more than one square mile. They feed mostly during early morning and late evening and spend the rest of the day idling in the shade. In late August the adults of both sexes begin their molt.

PRAIRIE chickens are infested by biting lice *(Mallophaga),* which lay their eggs at the bases of the feathers, usually in the region of the head and neck. The adult lice chew the feathers and irritate the skin of the host, inducing scratching.

THE BIRDS rid themselves of lice by means of frequent dust baths. The fine particles of dust are said to suffocate the pests by clogging their respiratory tubes.

I N GENERAL, prairie chickens are relatively free of disease-producing organisms, but occasionally some birds are killed by the disease commonly known as "blackhead." Livers of such birds show the sunken, reddish-gray lesions caused by the protozoan parasites *(Histomonas)*. Blackhead is common in domestic turkeys, which range freely over many areas inhabited by prairie chickens, and it is possible that the disease is transmitted to the latter by infected turkey droppings.

PREDATION does not present a serious hazard to prairie chickens in Missouri. Marsh hawks are often regarded as serious predators by local residents, but as a matter of fact, although they harass prairie chickens, they almost never kill them. The periods of spring and fall booming are also periods of marsh-hawk migration in this state, and most of these hawks are seen then. Cooper's hawks and red foxes are known to take prairie chickens occasionally, but the only important predator on the species in Missouri is Man.

As summer draws to a close and the shorter autumn days arrive, the chickens begin to gather into flocks of the separate sexes. The cocks resume their visits to the booming grounds, where they convene daily on some, although not all, of the sites used in the spring. In the morning from half an hour before until about an hour and a half after sunrise, and in the evening from about half an hour before sunset until dusk, they duplicate in many respects their spring courtship display. The numbers of cocks coming to the fall grounds closely approximate those seen in the spring. In years of high population and in densely populated areas as many as a hundred males have been seen on one fall booming ground.

FALL booming ground sites, in general, are the same as those used in the spring, although the exact part of the ground used in the fall may be slightly different, because of changes in the height and density of cover. In the case shown here, for example, the field at the left of the photograph was the spring booming ground shown under cultivation. When the birds came together again early in the fall, instead of using this field which had grown up to clover, grass, and weeds after the barley harvest, they selected the adjoining field beyond the fence, which had been freshly plowed for winter wheat. The new site was used until November. By that time the cover on the original location had been flattened by weather and cattle and many of the cocks returned to it.

EARLY in September, when the first cocks
return to the booming grounds, most of them have not completed
their molt. The feathers of the pinnae are still partly or entirely within their sheaths and new feathers are just beginning to appear on the
legs. The birds present a bob-tailed appearance because the new tail
feathers have not yet grown out. At this stage the sexes closely re-
semble each other.

DURING the first few weeks of the autumn gathering, booming is feeble and infrequent. At first there is no dancing, and the air sacs and eyebrows are not prominent. By early October the new tail feathers are fully grown but the pinnae are still short.

As each bird completes his molt, booming and dancing increase in vigor and the air sacs and eyebrows take on the same brilliant orange color as they showed in the spring. By the end of October, all the males are resplendent in their new plumage.

THE ESTABLISHMENT of territories also is a gradual process in the fall. The males which have molted earliest are the first to begin fighting, but by mid-November nearly all of them have established their territories.

THE PRAIRIE chicken uses the same calls and fighting behavior in the fall territorial disputes as in those of the spring.

I<small>N</small> <small>THE</small> midst of a round of feinting and sparring, one of the contestants may spring into the air and attempt to pounce upon his adversary below.

In contrast to the general lack of activity on the booming ground early in the fall, during the frosty mornings of November nearly all of the males are engaged in territorial fighting or booming. The autumn gatherings are composed mostly of males. Females appear occasionally, either singly or in small flocks, where they spend most of their time sitting quietly or preening themselves. Now and then a hen wanders among the displaying males, seemingly indifferent to their attentions, and there are no attempts at mating.

Departure of the birds from the booming ground in the morning is usually simultaneous, and the birds fly directly to nearby fields where they feed on grain, late insects, and weed seeds. At mid-day they drift away from the feeding areas and spend their time idling in the warmth of the autumn sunshine. There is a second feeding period in the afternoon before the birds return to the booming ground. This bird shows the loss of a considerable tuft of feathers from the rump as a mark of fall combat.

IF THERE is a severe and prolonged storm in November or December, there are no more regular visitors to the booming ground. Only a few males return occasionally during periods of milder weather and continue their characteristic activities, but less vigorously than before.

A FLOCK of prairie chickens flies together to its roosting place; once there, the birds scatter and each makes an individual "form." The form is about seven inches in diameter, usually with a floor of matted vegetation and, in the morning, the nightly accumulation of droppings. A new form is made each night.

GOOD roosting sites like this one are indispensable to prairie chickens because they roost on the ground in open country. Land-use practices which tend to reduce or destroy the amount of necessary cover are late-season mowing, burning, overgrazing, and cultivation.

IN THE winter, fields with suitable roosting cover close to good feeding grounds like the one in this photograph, attract large numbers of prairie chickens.

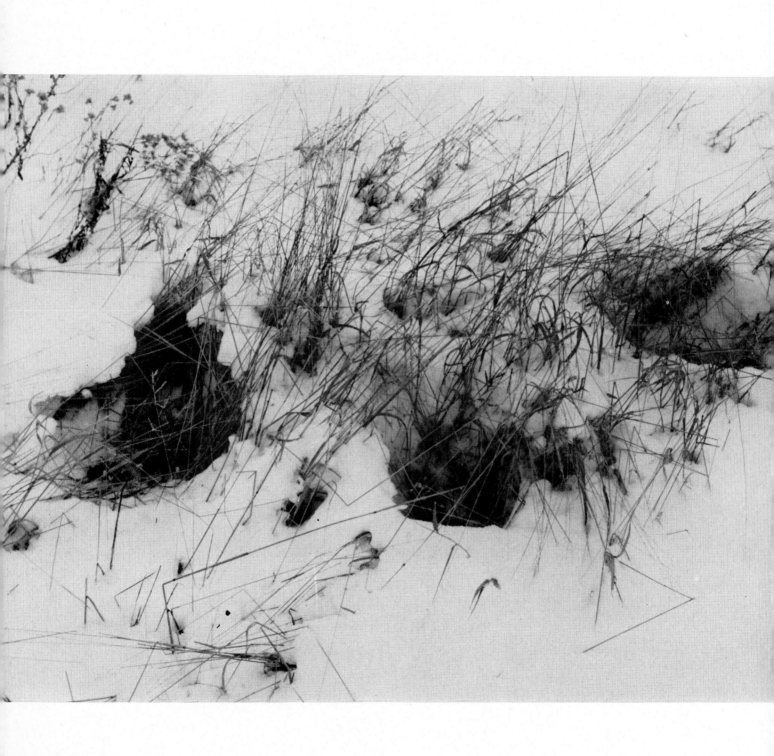

As winter sets in, roosting cover becomes sparse and the chickens are obliged to make the most of whatever small patches they can find.

I F SNOW falls during the night, the birds remain where they are, bursting out at daybreak.

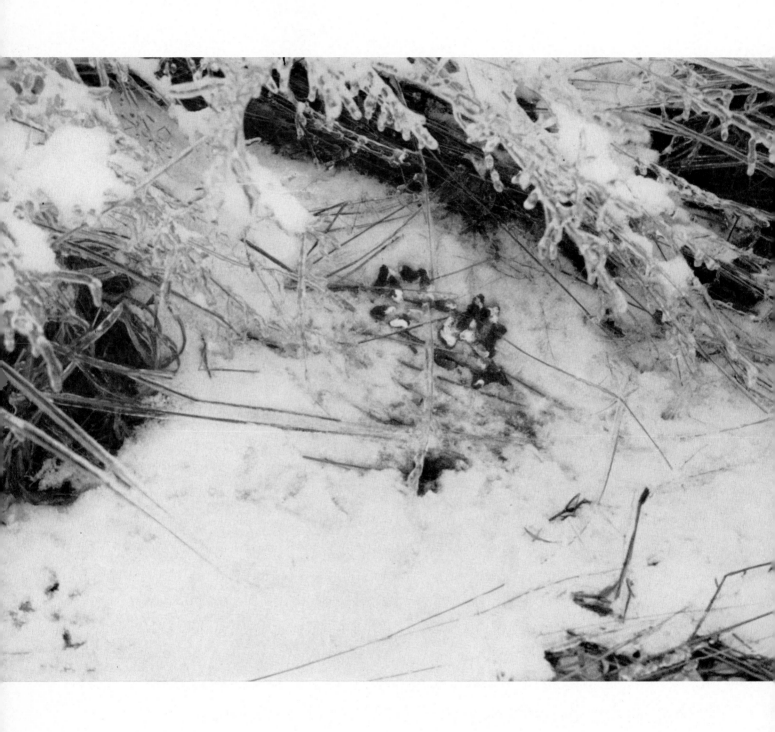

FORTUNATELY, ice storms and thick crusts are rare in Missouri. When they occur and the birds can not make roosting forms in the snow, they avail themselves of the protection afforded by overhanging slough grass in the swales.

For their daily periods of idling during the winter, prairie chickens usually frequent the same type of cover that they use for roosting. However, it need not be so high or so dense.

THE AVERAGE daily "cruising radius" of a flock during the winter takes it over about one square mile, although this radius is lengthened or shortened by the distance between feeding grounds and roosts.

DURING severe winter weather the flocks unite into larger groups composed of both sexes. In good prairie chicken country it is not uncommon to find a flock containing as many as two hundred and fifty or more birds. Although a flock seldom ranges over more than one square mile in a day, it may cover an area of five square miles or more in the course of a week.

From September through April, prairie chickens feed principally upon plant matter. In the summer, however, insects may constitute as much as forty percent of the food eaten, and many of these are economically destructive.

THE BIRDS depend upon culitvated grains for their principal food during the winter months. Cane, corn, and lespedeza are staple items.

When the snow is not too deep, prairie chickens still glean their food from fields where waste grain has been scattered during the harvest. There is a plentiful supply throughout their range in Missouri.

When green foods are made inaccessible by the snow, a flock frequently spends much of its time in trees, where the birds browse upon the tender buds. As many as a hundred birds may alight in a single large tree.

PRAIRIE chicken range in the extreme north-eastern part of the state is found on ridgetops and slopes along the numerous tributaries of the Mississippi River. Most of these are on strips of a "Grundy-like" soil a mile or so wide between the river-breaks.

THE RANGE in the central part of northeastern Missouri occupies a flat, poorly-drained area characterized by a hard-pan clay subsoil. Although this prairie soil (Putnam Silt Loam) is only moderately fertile, it is widely cultivated because of its level topography.

THE GENTLY-ROLLING prairie of north-central Missouri contains the largest occupied areas in the state. Extensive tracts are now in permanent tame grass because the rolling topography and the erosive nature of this type of prairie soil (Shelby Loam) will not support continuous cropping.

PRAIRIE chickens are found also on the gently-rolling prairie of south-central Missouri. Here large areas are maintained in permanent tame or wild grass because the soil (Oswego Silt Loam) is best suited to this use.

THE ONLY large expanses of virgin prairie remaining in Missouri are in the southwestern part of the state. Prairie chickens live here among the big and little bluestem grasses and other native flora because, fortunately for them all, the low fertility of the Cherokee Silt Loam has never encouraged cultivation.

THE PRINCIPAL agricultural use of the land occupied by prairie chickens is for the production of cattle. This involves the maintenance of large areas of grass in a system of permanent pasture.

PRAIRIE chickens depend upon both the quality and extent of permanent grassland. Some occupied areas contain as little as thirty-nine percent of grassland, others as much as eighty-four percent. Much of the land not in grass is planted to corn and small grains.

Hayland bears an important relationship to nesting and roosting requirements. Areas that produce crops of hay provide much of the cover so necessary to the success of these activities.

The wild grasses of the southwestern prairie are used more for hay than for grazing. In northern Missouri, however, the timothy, bluegrass, and redtop are used to a greater extent for pasturage.

WHEN mowing takes place late in the summer, its effect upon the welfare of prairie chickens may be serious. Not only does it reduce the amount of nesting cover for the next spring, but also vegetation is destroyed which the birds would otherwise use as roosting cover during the winter. Leaving some areas unmowed helps to prevent this loss.

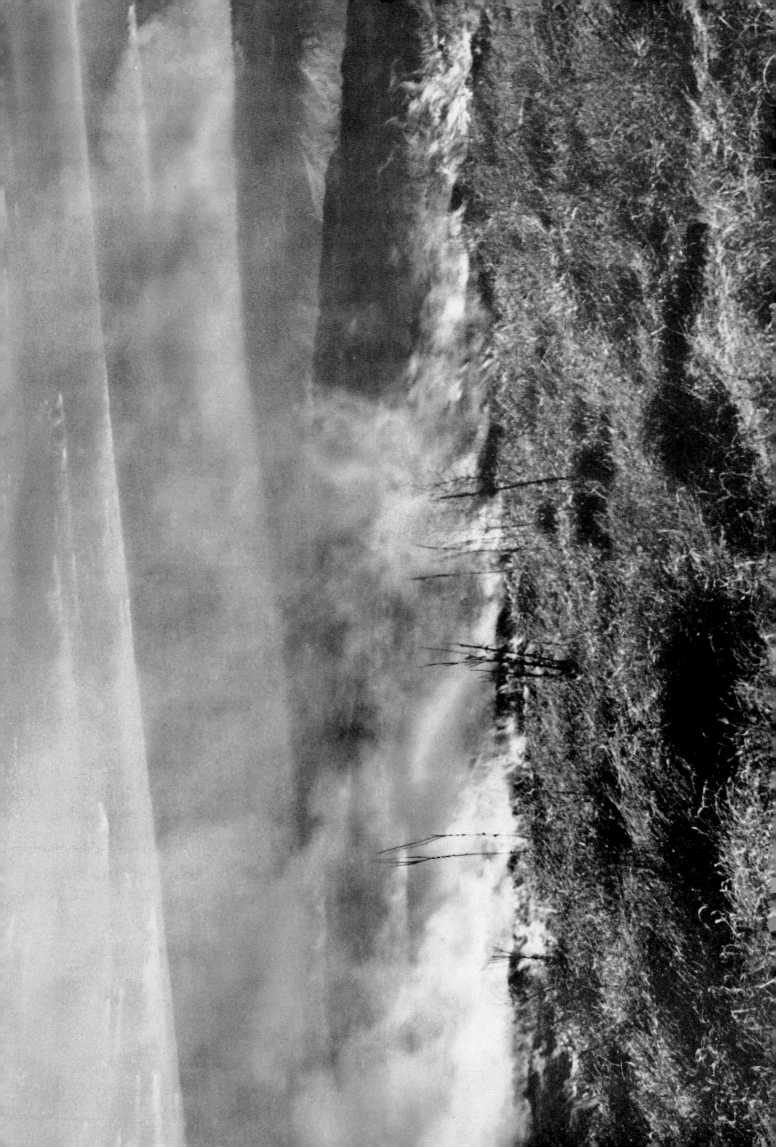

THE INDISCRIMINATE burning of hayland to remove dead vegetation is a widespread practice that is detrimental not only to prairie chickens and other wildlife but also to the soil. If there must be burning, at least it should take place under conditions permitting adequate control.

OVERGRAZING is almost universal on the Missouri prairies. More wisely-administered grazing would benefit the soil; also it would provide and improve roosting and nesting cover for prairie birds.

Destruction of the permanent sod on a soil suited for little but grass is not intelligent use of the land.

Lack of water is seldom a limiting factor in the lives of prairie chickens. In normal years dew, succulent vegetation, and temporary natural pools like this one probably fulfill the birds' requirements for water.

Deep and permanent ponds are needed on grassland that is used to its best advantage as a producer of livestock. Such ponds are helpful to prairie chickens and other wildlife at all times; in drought years they are indispensable.

THE PROBLEM of winter food on prairie chicken ranges is not one of creating additional sources, since ordinarily food is abundant. Rather, it is a problem of reducing local and concentrated damage. When the general population reaches a density of more than ten birds per square mile, large flocks of birds consume a good deal of cultivated grain, sometimes causing the farmers to complain and call for control.

Live-trapping as a method of controlling local depredations has not proved practicable in Missouri. The abundance of cultivated food everywhere makes it impossible to lure into baited traps enough birds to relieve the situation. However, trapping is of some value in procuring birds for scientific study or for limited restocking purposes.

ALTHOUGH a completely closed season has been in effect in Missouri since 1907, illegal kill continues to be a serious deterrent to the increase of prairie chickens throughout this range. Law enforcement has improved greatly in recent years. While this, in itself, cannot restore birds when essential environmental conditions are lacking, it is making possible a more rapid increase than could have occurred without it.

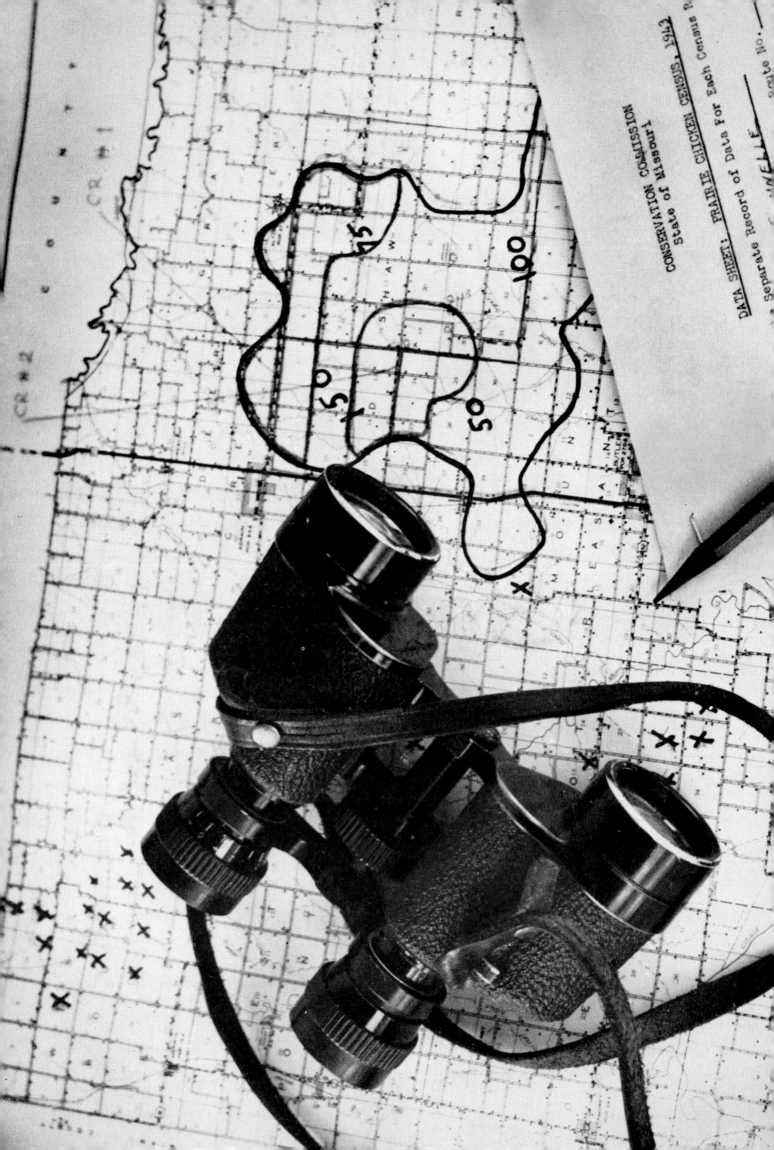

A MEANS of measuring, with reasonable accuracy, the current population of a wildlife species is essential to sound management. In Missouri a practical method of censusing the spring population of prairie chickens has been developed and is used annually. It is based upon a count of birds seen and heard on the spring booming grounds.

An EDUCATIONAL program designed to teach rural boys and girls the principles and practices of wildlife conservation is carried on by the Conservation Commission in cooperation with the State Department of Education and other agencies, and it is helpful in assuring the future of the prairie chicken. Concrete examples, in the form of demonstration areas, carry weight with adults as well.

THE FUTURE of the prairie chicken in Missouri is in the hands of all the people of the state, but it depends most of all upon those who use the soil.